ISBN 0-09-942110-0

Humour
UK £1.75
Australia $5.50*
Canada $4.50*
*recommended price

00175

9 780099 421108

KW-054-070

— A DIAMOND IS FOREVER —

I didn't mind the roller skates so much – it was the duck which threw me

GOD THROWS
DOWN LOTS OF
FRECKLES AND
MOST OF THEM
FALL ON ME

Helen Cusack

6.50pm.

6.55pm.

7pm.

HELEN CUSACK
1982

— SHOPPING AT JEZEBEL'S —

The Architect at Home | Homes designed by the Architect

Rememberance Sunday . . . . The Queen lays a wreath.

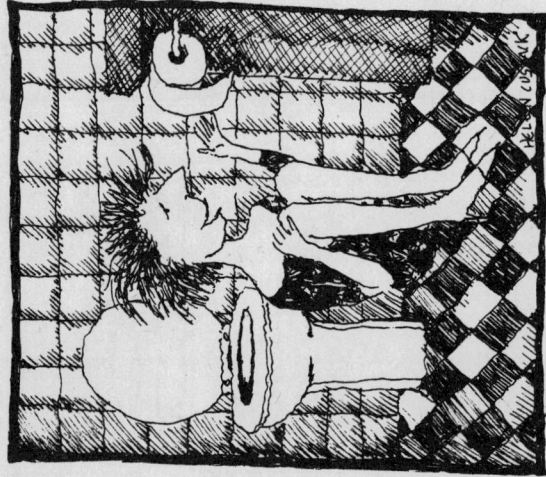

my need for intellectual
stimulation
torments my soul
but I have nice
long talks
with the toilet roll

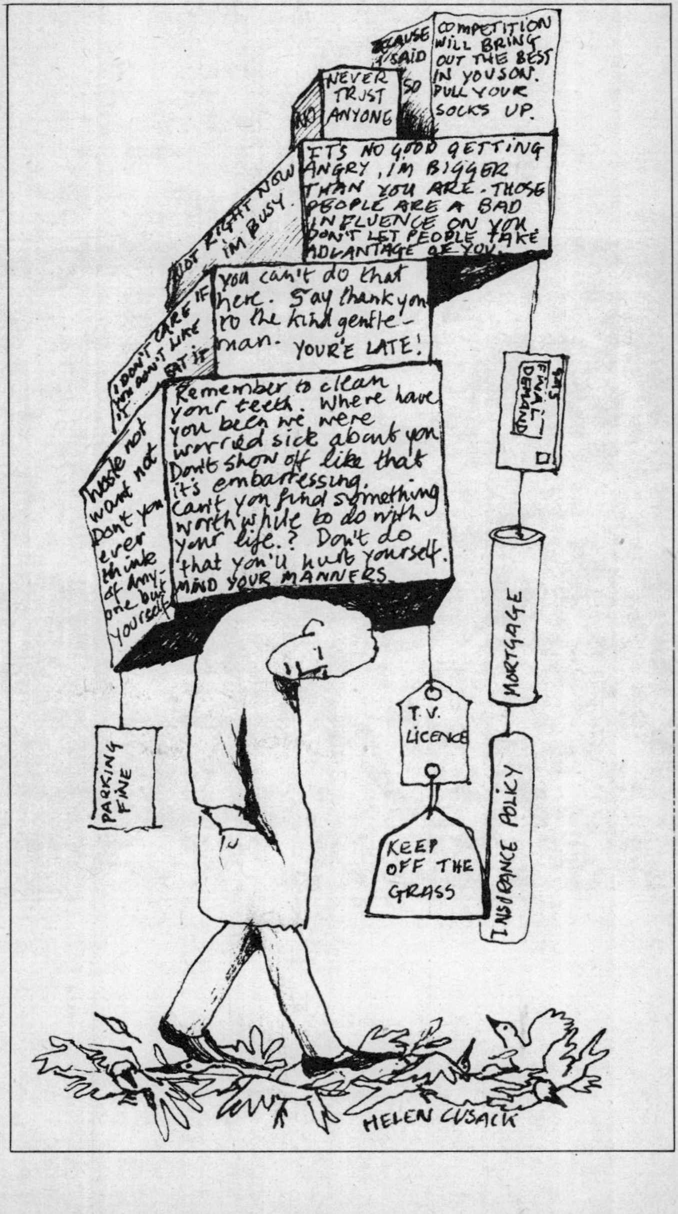

Bravo!

Helen Cusack

— THE BORING WIFE —

— A PRESENT FROM RICK —

YOU'RE STILL ANGRY BECAUSE WE DIDN'T GET A HOLIDAY THIS YEAR — AREN'T YOU.

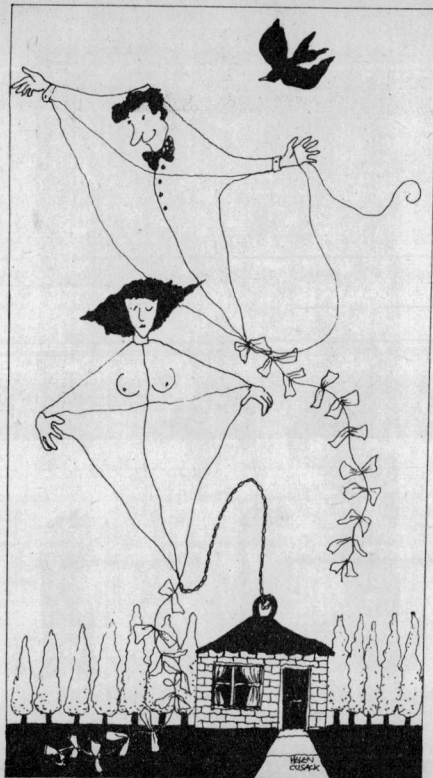

— GOSSIP —

Helen Cusack

THE OLD DEAR PARK

Helen Cusack

Helen Cusack

HELEN
CUSACK 1982

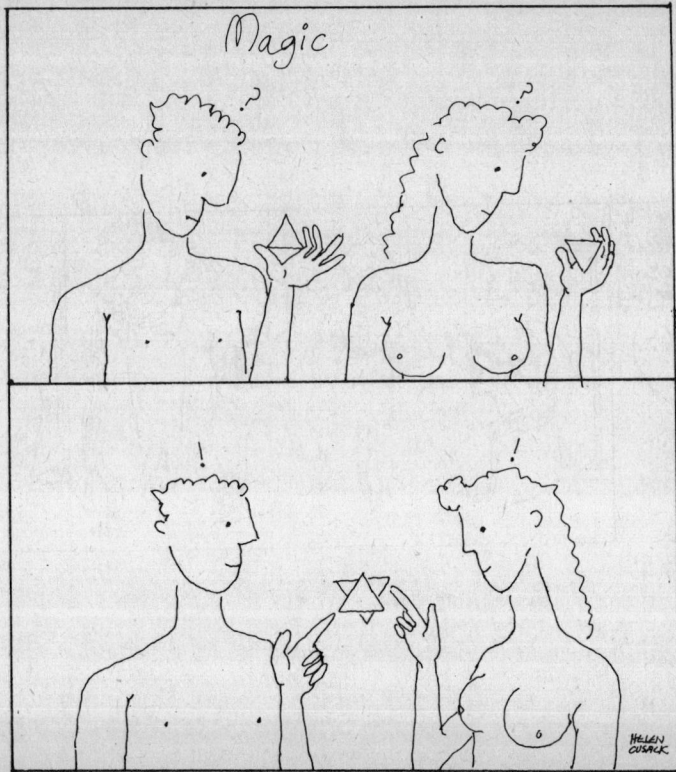

MEN APPLAUDING AFTER AN IMMACULATE CONCEPTION

— DOUBLE STANDARDS —

HELEN
CUSACK

— THE FLIGHT OF THE WOMEN —

— FAIR EXCHANGE IS NO ROBBERY —

HELEN CUSACK.

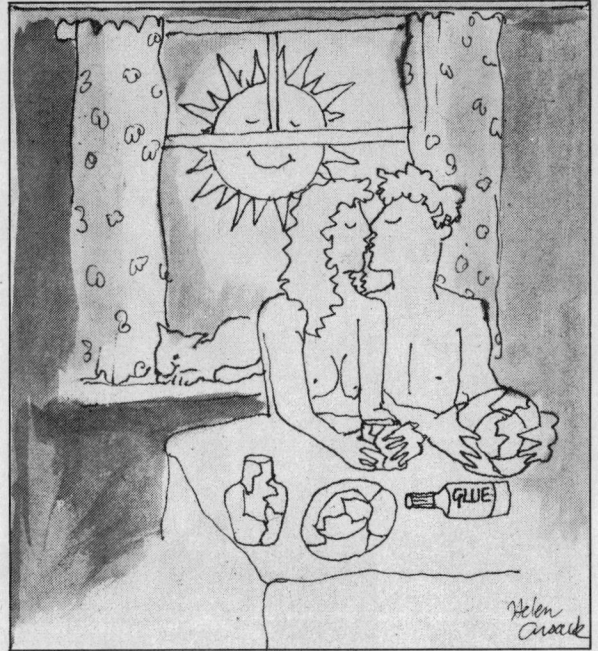

— THE PATH OF TRUE LOVE —

I TOLD NIGEL THAT I NEEDED HIS INTEREST AND SUPPORT - AND AS USUAL HE DIDN'T UNDERSTAND WHAT I MEANT

Helen Cusack

— YOU EAT WHAT YOU ARE —

I can see we're going to
have to build up your
confidence, my dear

O.K. — so you've had a few knocks this year.

Helen Cusack

IT'S IMPORTANT TO RECEIVE A FRIENDLY GREETING AFTER A HARD DAY'S WORK

AND A GOOD, STRONG CUP OF TEA

LIGHT ON DARK WINTER EVENINGS

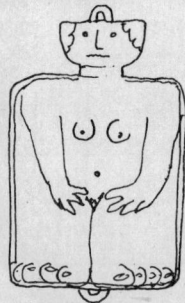

AND A WARM SPOT IN THE BED

— USES FOR WOMEN AROUND THE HOUSE —

— ROUND IS BEAUTIFUL —

— GOOD MORNING —

HELEN
CUSACK

I told you that after a while he wouldn't seem
quite as amusing.

Helen Cusack

IT WASN'T UNTIL I READ THROUGH MY DIARY

THAT I REALIZED WHY SO FEW PEOPLE UNDERSTAND ME

HELEN CUSACK

HELEN CUSACK

1983

— THE OUTSIDER —

Ellie is taking puberty very seriously

—JOGGING THE MEMORY—

— LOGIC —

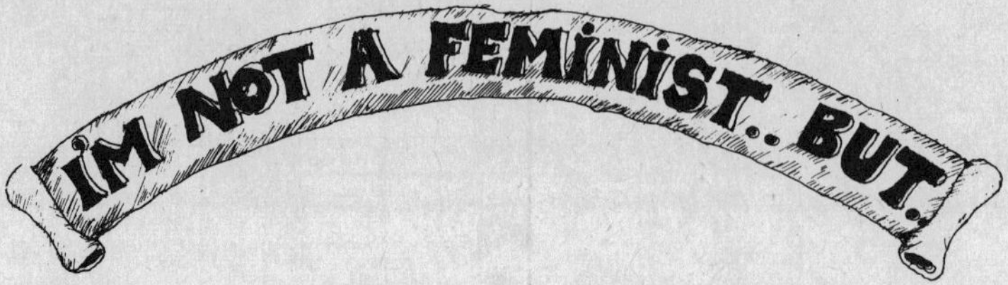
I'M NOT A FEMINIST.. BUT..

Arrow Books Limited
17-21 Conway Street, London W1P 6JD

An imprint of the Hutchinson Publishing Group

London Melbourne Sydney Auckland Johannesburg
and agencies throughout the world

First published in Great Britain by Arrow Books 1985

Printed and bound in Great Britain by
Anchor Brendon Limited, Tiptree, Essex

ISBN 0 09 942110 0

I'M NOT A FEMINIST.. BUT.

Helen Cusack

ARROW BOOKS

Artist, mother, Cancerian and not a feminist, Helen Cusack is a young painter and cartoonist whose work has appeared in *City Limits* and *Sour Cream* as well as other papers and periodicals. She lives in London.